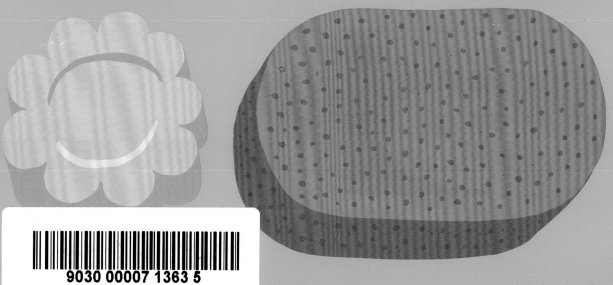

7/20

RED SPOT

~~HEATH~~
J
616
CARR

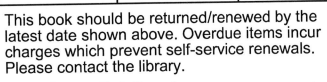
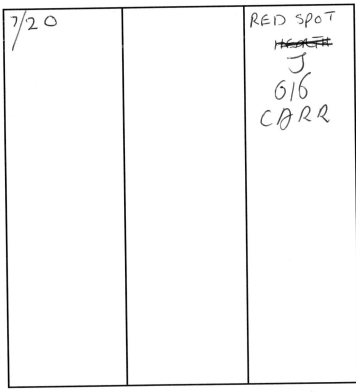

For Coco, Mabel, Delilah and Ivy - M.C.
Dedicated to the amazing people who work for the NHS!

Published in the UK by Scholastic Children's Books, 2020
Euston House, 24 Eversholt Street,
London, NW1 1DB
A division of Scholastic Limited

London ~ New York ~ Toronto ~ Sydney ~ Auckland
Mexico City ~ New Delhi ~ Hong Kong

SCHOLASTIC and associated logos are trademarks
and/or registered trademarks of Scholastic Inc.

Text © Matt Carr, 2020
Illustrations © Matt Carr, 2020

The right of Matt Carr to be identified as the author
and illustrator of this work has been asserted by him
under the Copyright, Designs and Patents Act 1988.

ISBN 978 07023 0565 8

A CIP catalogue record for this book is
available from the British Library.

Printed by CPI Colour
110 Beddington Lane, Croydon, CR0 4YY

Papers used by Scholastic Children's Books are
made from wood grown in sustainable forests.

10 9 8 7 6 5 4 3 2 1

This is a work of fiction. Names, characters, places incidents
and dialogues are products of the author's imagination or
are used fictitiously. Any resemblance to actual people,
living or dead, events or locales is entirely coincidental.

www.scholastic.co.uk

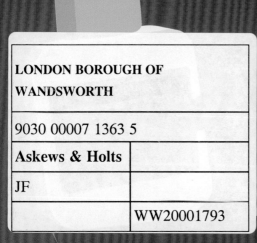

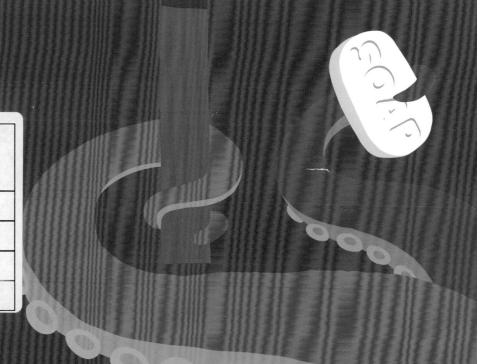

At school the kids
    were running wild,
        the thing that
            kids do best ...

when Mrs Moo came into the room with a very special guest.

"Doctorpus Doris is here today, for a really important chat. So make sure that you're listening and sitting on the mat!"

"I'd like to tell you all about
something VERY, VERY small.

In fact they are so TEENY WEENY
you can't see them at all!"

"We like to call them **GERMS!** And it's you they want to hug ...

... but the only trouble is, they can give you a nasty bug!"

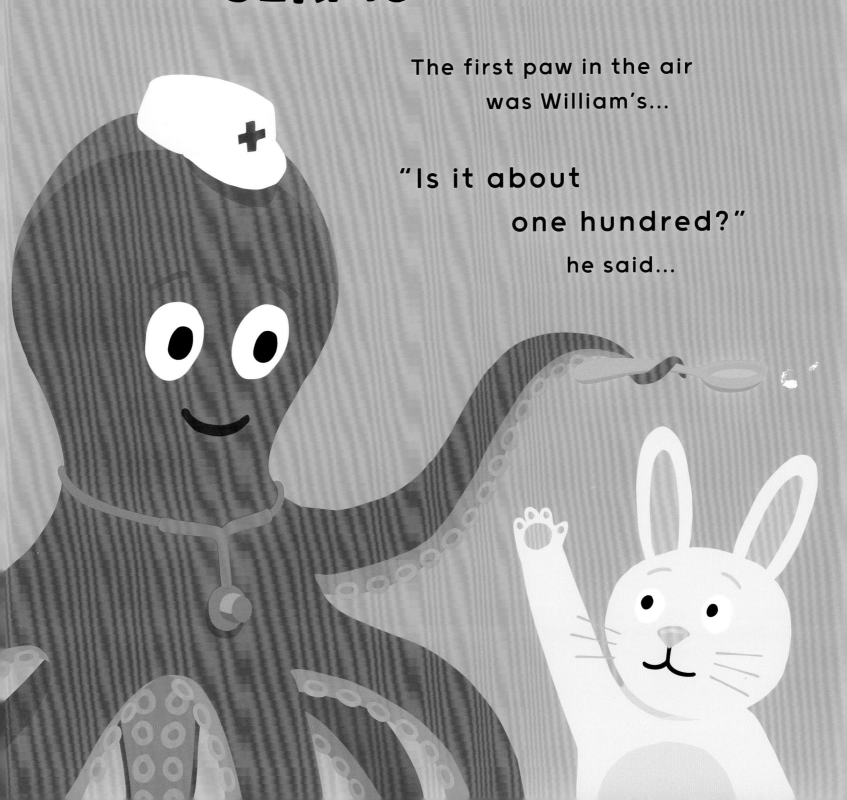

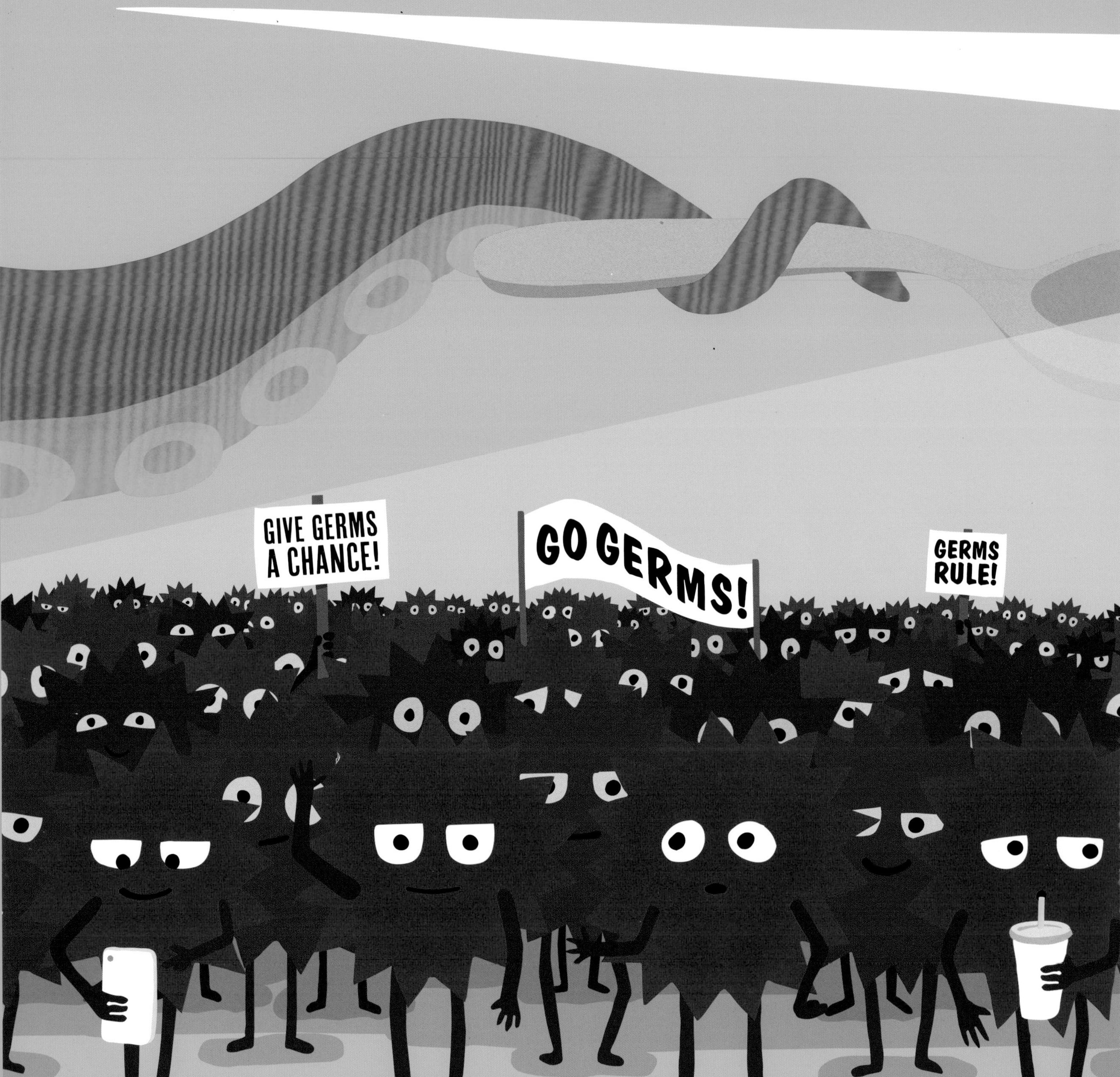
GIVE GERMS
A CHANCE!
GO GERMS!
GERMS
RULE!

"But the good news is, there's a simple thing that little germs can't stand...

If you don't want them to hang around, all you do is ...

WASH YOUR HANDS!"

"Or if you're in the garden with Mum, potting up some plants..."

"You **WASH YOUR HANDS** when you get inside."

"Don't give those germs a chance!"

"And Kenny, what about in the toilet, when you've done a WEE or a POO?"

"Do you **WASH YOUR HANDS,** Miss?"

"**YES!** It's the only thing to do!"

DORIS'S HANDY HAND-WASHING SONG!

WASH YOUR HANDS it's EASY,
WASH YOUR HANDS it's FUN,
WASH YOUR HANDS so you don't
pass on GERMS to anyone!
Use lots of SOAP and WATER
Then DRY them when you're done.
It's the SIMPLE way
to KEEP GERMS AT BAY,

WASH YOUR HANDS, EVERYONE!

Sing this when you wash your hands to help you give them a super scrub!

GIVE YOUR PAWS A PROPER PAMPER!

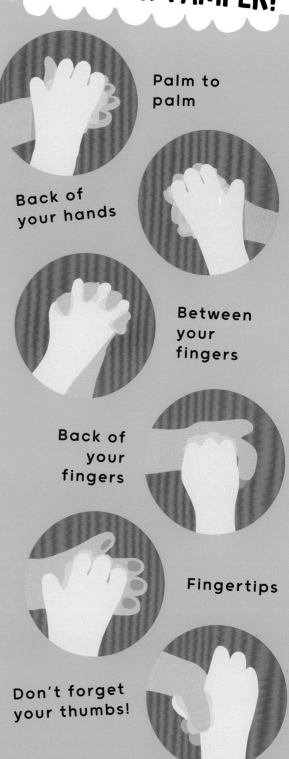

Palm to palm

Back of your hands

Between your fingers

Back of your fingers

Fingertips

Don't forget your thumbs!

Lavender
SOAP

Savonette
De Luxe

Soap
on a
Rope

Orange
Crush

HANDY WASH

Raspberry

Hand
Cream

100% NATURAL

Liquid
Soap

SOAP